**Editors**

Polly Hoffman

Gisela Lee

Mary S. Jones

**Managing Editor**

Karen J. Goldfluss, M.S. Ed.

**Illustrator**

Ken Tunnel

**Cover Artist**

Lesley Palmer

**Art Coordinator**

Kevin Barnes

**Creative Director**

CJae Froshay

**Imaging**

Rosa C. See

**Publisher**

Mary D. Smith, M.S. Ed.

# How to Work with Probability and Statistics

## Grades 5-6

**Author**

*Kathleen N. Kopp, M.S. Ed.*

***Teacher Created Resources, Inc.***

6421 Industry Way

Westminster, CA 92683

www.teachercreated.com

**ISBN: 978-1-57690-960-7**

*©2005 Teacher Created Resources, Inc.*

Reprinted, 2009

Made in U.S.A.

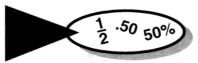

# Table of Contents

**How to Use This Book** . . . . . . . . . . . . . . . . . . 3
**NCTM Standards** . . . . . . . . . . . . . . . . . . . . . 4

**Unit 1**
How to Determine Probability . . . . . . . . . . . . 5
Practice Identifying Certain and
    Impossible Events . . . . . . . . . . . . . . . . . . . 6
Practice Identifying Likely, Unlikely, and
    Equally Likely Events . . . . . . . . . . . . . . . . 7
Practice Making Decisions with Probability . . . 8

**Unit 2**
How to Show Probability . . . . . . . . . . . . . . . . 9
Practice Showing Probability with Fractions . . 10
Practice Showing Probability with Decimals
    and Percents . . . . . . . . . . . . . . . . . . . . . . 11
Practice Showing Probability in Three Ways . . 12

**Unit 3**
How to Compare Outcomes . . . . . . . . . . . . . . 13
Practice Comparing Probabilities . . . . . . . . . . 14
Practice Multiplying to Determine Probability 15
Practice Drawing a Tree Diagram
    or Making a List . . . . . . . . . . . . . . . . . . . 16

**Unit 4**
How to Make Predictions with Probability
    and Data . . . . . . . . . . . . . . . . . . . . . . . . . 17
Practice Making Predictions
    with Probability . . . . . . . . . . . . . . . . . . . 18
Practice Making Predictions with Data . . . . . . 19
Practice Making Predictions with
    Different Data . . . . . . . . . . . . . . . . . . . . . 20

**Unit 5**
How to Use Ratios . . . . . . . . . . . . . . . . . . . . 21
Practice Showing Ratios in Three Ways . . . . . 22
Practice Calculating Equivalent Ratios . . . . . . 23
Practice Using Ratios to Show Odds . . . . . . . 24

**Unit 6**
How to Chart Statistics . . . . . . . . . . . . . . . . . 25
Practice Using Ratios to Determine Fairness . . 26

Practice Using Charts, Data, and Ratios to
    Determine Fairness . . . . . . . . . . . . . . . . . 27
Practice Using Ratios to Show
    Large Quantities . . . . . . . . . . . . . . . . . . . 28

**Unit 7**
How to Calculate Mean and Range . . . . . . . . 29
Practice Calculating Mean . . . . . . . . . . . . . . 30
Practice Finding the Range and
    Charting Data . . . . . . . . . . . . . . . . . . . . . 31
Practice Estimating the Mean and Range . . . . 32

**Unit 8**
How to Average with Median and Mode . . . . . 33
Practice Finding the Median and Mode . . . . . . 34
Practice Finding the Median and
    Mode from Graphs . . . . . . . . . . . . . . . . . 35
Practice Experimenting to Find
    the Median and Mode . . . . . . . . . . . . . . . 36

**Unit 9**
How to Chart Data to Find Median
    and Mode . . . . . . . . . . . . . . . . . . . . . . . . 37
Practice Calculating Median and Mode
    with Stem-and-Leaf Plots . . . . . . . . . . . . 38
Practice Calculating Median and Mode
    Using Frequency Charts . . . . . . . . . . . . . 39
Practice Estimating Median and Mode
    for Large Quantities . . . . . . . . . . . . . . . . 40

**Unit 10**
Practice Working with Combinations . . . . . . . 41
Practice Simulations and Combinations . . . . . 42

**Unit 11** (Brain Teasers)
Outliers . . . . . . . . . . . . . . . . . . . . . . . . . . . 43
Tricky Averages . . . . . . . . . . . . . . . . . . . . . 44

**Unit 12** (Technology)
Spreadsheet Files . . . . . . . . . . . . . . . . . . . . 45
All About Sharks . . . . . . . . . . . . . . . . . . . . 46

**Answer Key** . . . . . . . . . . . . . . . . . . . . . . 47

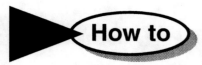 

## A Note to Teachers and Parents

Welcome to the "How to" math series! You have chosen one of several books designed to give your children the information and practice they need to acquire important concepts in specific areas of math. The goal of the "How to" math books is to give children an extra boost as they work toward mastery of the math skills established by the National Council of Teachers of Mathematics (NCTM) and outlines in grade-level scope-and-sequence guidelines.

This book is intended to be used by teachers and parents for a variety of purposes and needs. Each of the individual units contains one or more "How to" pages and two or more practice pages. The "How to" section of each unit precedes the practice pages and provides needed information such as a concept or math rule review, important terms and formulas to remember, or step-by-step guidelines necessary for using the practice pages. While most "How to" pages are written for direct use by the children, in some lower-grade level books, these pages are presented as instructional pages or direct lessons to be used by a teacher or parent prior to introducing the practice pages.

## About This Book

*How to Work with Probability and Statistics: Grades 4–6* introduces the concepts of probability and data analysis to the first-time learner, then extends these concepts to the relationship between data and statistics and how they apply to the real world for advanced learners.

The activities in this book will help your children learn important new skills or reinforce skills already learned in the following areas:

- Determining the likelihood of outcomes, both in words and as quantities expressed as percents, decimals, and fractions.
- Creating and analyzing diagrams, charts, graphs, and tables to determine probable outcomes.
- Analyzing data to predict outcomes.
- Comparing probable outcomes of singular and compound events.
- Expressing outcomes as ratios.
- Calculating equivalent ratios.
- Calculating mean, median, range, and mode.
- Collecting, organizing, and analyzing data to discover averages.

Each subsequent concept builds upon the learning of the previous skills. Teacher and parents are encouraged to complete the book in order as it is presented here, unless students are in need of remedial instruction in specific areas.

Regardless of their ability to add, subtract, multiply, and divide, students may complete the practice pages following the concepts presented on "How to" pages with ease. Students may use a calculator when working with higher numbers unless their computation skills are in need of remediation.

Once having completed this book, students will feel like professional statisticians ready to apply their learning to all areas of their lives.

*How to Work with Probability and Statistics: Grades 4–6* matches a number of NCTM standards in the following areas:

## Statistics

The activities in this book allow students to explore statistics in real-world situations. This includes the collection, organization, and description of data, and the construction and interpretation of charts, tables, and graphs. Students also must make practical and sensible decisions based on the analysis of data and provide arguments for their decision.

## Probability

The activities in this book provide model situations in which students must determine probabilities and express results in several ways. Students must also make predictions based on probable experiment and theory, and justify decisions based on results.

## Computation and Estimation

The activities in this book require students to compute and estimate both statistical and probable results with whole numbers, fractions, and decimals. This includes computation and estimation in isolation as well as in the solution of real-world situations.

## Problem Solving

The activities in this book offer a wide array of open-ended, real-world problems for which students must use their mathematical expertise to provide solutions. As part of the problem-solving process, students meaningfully apply their problem-solving skills to verify and interpret results and justify decisions based on these results.

## Other Standards

The activities in this book provide a range of additional skill application such as mathematical reasoning and proportions. This book also provides connections to other subject areas and to the world outside the classroom and the identification and interpretation of patterns and functions through the use of charts, tables, and graphs.

## Facts to Know

**Probability** is a term used in mathematics to explain the chance that a future event will occur, or the likelihood of an outcome. Think to yourself. What is the likelihood of you eating ice cream today? Will it definitely happen? Will it definitely not happen? Will it perhaps happen? Probability helps us assign a numerical value to the likelihood of future events or outcomes.

 Some events, such as the sun rising each day, are **certain**. They have a probability of 100% or 1.

Some events, such as a dog flying through the air, are **impossible**. They have a probability of 0% or 0.

Some events, such as catching a cold, may occur or may not occur. Depending on a number of outside influences, this particular event may be **likely** or **unlikely**. This likelihood may be assigned a number between 0% and 100% or between 0 and 1. For example, if you are usually pretty healthy, and you have been eating right all winter and dressing appropriately when you go outside, you may think you only have about a 10% chance of catching a cold. But if you have been around a lot of friends and family members who have had colds, or if you usually catch a cold every winter, you may think you have about an 80% chance of catching a cold.

For some events, which have only two outcomes, such as flipping a coin, the likelihood of either outcome is **equally likely**. This means there is an equal chance that these events will occur or not occur. They fall right in the middle and have a probability of 50%, .5, or 1/2.

  When flipping a coin, either heads or tails will appear. The likelihood of each outcome is equal.

Similarly, if the forecast calls for a 50% chance of rain, the meteorologist is telling you that there is an **equally likely** chance of rain and no rain.

**Certain** events will definitely occur. They have a probability of 100% or 1.

**Impossible** events will definitely not occur. They have a probability of 0% or 0.

**Directions:** Read each event below. Decide and circle whether it is certain or impossible. Write the probability of this event occurring on the line.

| | | | |
|---|---|---|---|
| **Example:** Elvis releasing a new hit single | Certain | (Impossible) | <u>0%</u> |

1. rocks falling from clouds — Certain — Impossible — _____

2. bees making honey — Certain — Impossible — _____

3. you going home from school today — Certain — Impossible — _____

4. the United States celebrating its independence on July 4th — Certain — Impossible — _____

5. water running downhill — Certain — Impossible — _____

6. pulling a blue marble from a bag of only red marbles — Certain — Impossible — _____

7. an all-night diner being open 24 hours — Certain — Impossible — _____

8. the date February 33rd — Certain — Impossible — _____

9. George Washington, the first President of the United States, running for office next year — Certain — Impossible — _____

10. you eating a pencil for dinner tonight — Certain — Impossible — _____

**In Your Own Words**

**Directions:** List three certain and three impossible events that were not mentioned already.

| **These Events Are Certain** | **These Events Are Impossible** |
|---|---|
| _____ | _____ |
| _____ | _____ |
| _____ | _____ |

Events that may or may not occur are **likely** or **unlikely**. They have a probability between 0% and 100% or between 0 and 1.

Events that have an equal chance of occurring or not occurring are **equally likely** and have a probability of 50%, .5, or 1/2.

**Directions:** Read each event below. Decide and circle whether it is likely, unlikely, or if there is an equally likely chance that it will occur or not occur. Decide (in your opinion) the probability of this event occurring and write it on the line.

| Example | | | | |
|---|---|---|---|---|
| The fire alarm going off at school today. | Likely | Unlikely | Equally Likely | 50% |

| | | | | |
|---|---|---|---|---|
| 1. You going in your house through the front door instead of the back door. | Likely | Unlikely | Equally Likely | _____ |
| 2. You having a party this afternoon. | Likely | Unlikely | Equally Likely | _____ |
| 3. You eating pizza today. | Likely | Unlikely | Equally Likely | _____ |
| 4. You going to the store today. | Likely | Unlikely | Equally Likely | _____ |
| 5. You getting a new pet this week. | Likely | Unlikely | Equally Likely | _____ |
| 6. You having spaghetti for dinner. | Likely | Unlikely | Equally Likely | _____ |
| 7. Your family taking a long trip this year. | Likely | Unlikely | Equally Likely | _____ |
| 8. You becoming a doctor. | Likely | Unlikely | Equally Likely | _____ |
| 9. You voting as an adult. | Likely | Unlikely | Equally Likely | _____ |
| 10. You helping with the chores at home. | Likely | Unlikely | Equally Likely | _____ |

**In Your Own Words**

**Directions:** On the lines provided, write one likely event, one unlikely event, and one equally likely event. Write the probability that you think each event has on the lines provided.

This event is likely. It has a probability of _____.

_____

This event is unlikely. It has a probability of _____.

_____

This event has an equal chance of occurring or not occurring. It has a probability of _____.

_____

**Directions:** Use the terms you learned on page 5 to help explain your decisions for the following situations.

1. Glenda overheard on the radio that the weather forecast called for an 80% chance of rain. Should she pack her umbrella in her book bag?

   _____

   _____

   _____

2. Mark is playing a board game with his friend Albert. He needs to spin a 5 to win the game. He has a 10% chance of spinning the number he needs. Should he expect to win on this turn?

   _____

   _____

   _____

3. Reread situation number 2. Would Mark be more likely to win if his chance of spinning a 5 were 50% instead of 10%? Compare these two probabilities. How might a 50% chance at a win on this turn affect the game?

   _____

   _____

   _____

4. Erin expects a surprise party for her birthday. She is 95% sure this event will occur. Why might she feel almost certain?

   _____

   _____

   _____

5. James has a choice of getting either a hot dog or a hamburger for lunch. Can you correctly predict which he will receive? Why or why not?

   _____

   _____

   _____

6. Players of a popular carnival game win 30% of the time. Would you play this game if it cost only 25¢ to play? What if a play cost $1.00? Why or why not?

   _____

   _____

   _____

## Facts to Know

Use one of following three ways to show the likelihood of an outcome: a **fraction**, a **decimal**, or a **percent**.

### Probability as a Fraction

One way to show probability is with a **fraction**.

> The numerator shows ⟶ the number of ways an event can occur.
> The denominator shows ⟶ the total number of possible outcomes.

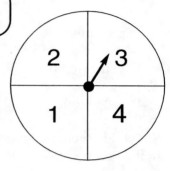

Example: What is the probability of spinning a *3* on the spinner to the right? First notice that all the spaces in the spinner are of equal size.

> Numerator ⟶ the number of ways to spin a 3 is 1.
> Denominator ⟶ the total number of possible outcomes is 4.
> Therefore, the probability (as a fraction) is $\frac{1}{4}$

### Probability as a Decimal

Another way to show probability is with a **decimal**. To show probability as a decimal, first show it as a fraction. Then, divide the numerator by the denominator. In the example above, the numerator 1 divided by the denominator 4 equals .25. The probability of spinning a 3 may be expressed as .25. **Note:** All probabilities written as a decimal are between 0 and 1.

### Probability as a Percent

The last way to show probability is as a **percent**. Using your decimal figure, multiply it by 100 and include a percent symbol. Using the same example used above, .25 x 100 = 25 so the probability of spinning a 3 is 25%.

| 1 | 3 | 1 |
|---|---|---|
| 3 | 5 | 3 |
| 1 | 3 | 1 |

What about the grid to the left? The probability of tossing a beanbag to land on a 1 is

**fraction**   $\dfrac{\text{possible ways}}{\text{total outcomes}} = \dfrac{4}{9}$

**decimal**   $4 \div 9 = .44$

**percent**   $.44 \times 100 = 44\%$

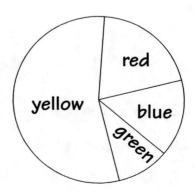

Look at the spinner to the right. Each space is not of equal size. You cannot determine the numerical probability of landing on any one color since each outcome is not equal.

## Facts to Know

**Directions:** Use what you have learned about showing probability as a fraction on page 9. Read each situation. Think about the occurrence of each event. Then, write the probability of each occurrence as a fraction.

A bag has two green marbles, two blue marbles, and one yellow marble. If you were to reach into the bag, write as a fraction what the probability would be that you would randomly select a:

**1.** blue marble _____

**2.** green marble _____

**3.** yellow marble _____

**4.** red marble _____

Six children entered a drawing to win a bike. John's name is in the box three times. Karen's name is in the box two times. Roger's name is in the box once. Sarah's name is in the box twice. Joe's name is in the box once. Linda's name is in the box once. Write the children's names on the cards below as described and determine the probability that . . .

**5.** John's name will be randomly picked. _____

**6.** Sarah's name will be randomly picked. _____

**7.** Joe's name will be randomly picked. _____

**8.** a boy's name will be randomly picked. _____

**9.** a girl's name will be randomly picked. _____

**10.** Whose name is most likely to be randomly picked? _____

**11.** Should Linda expect to be the winner of the bike? Explain your answer. _____

_____

_____

_____

Alphabet tiles are placed in a bag during a kindergarten lesson. Each student is asked to pull a tile at random to identify the letter, then, put it back. What is the probability that. . .

**12.** a vowel will be selected? _____

**13.** a consonant will be selected? _____

**14.** the letter "Y" will be selected? _____

**15.** the Greek letter "∑" will be selected? _____

**16.** a letter before "J" will be selected? _____

**17.** a letter in the word "pig" will be selected? _____

You can show the numerical probability of an event occurring as a **decimal** or **percent**. To find the **decimal**, first find the fractional probability, then divide the numerator by the denominator.

**Example:** fractional probability $= \frac{2}{5}$ ⟶ $2 \div 5 = .40$

To find the **percent**, multiply the decimal by 100 and add a percent sign.

**Example:** decimal probability $= .40$ ⟶ $.40 \times 100 = 40\%$

**Directions:** Look at each situation below. Calculate the probability of each event as a decimal and percent.

Jake decided to color his picture by selecting crayons from the box at random. There were 10 crayons in the box: blue, red, yellow, orange, green, purple, white, brown, black, and gray. Write the probability for each event.

|  | Decimal | Percent |
|---|---|---|
| **1.** Jake will color the duck blue. | _____ | _____ |
| **2.** Jake will color the sky orange. | _____ | _____ |
| **3.** Jake will color the tree a primary color. | _____ | _____ |
| **4.** Jake will color the cloud a color that starts with the letter "b". | _____ | _____ |

Gina went to the pet store to get a new puppy. When she got there, she couldn't decide which one to get. So she asked the storeowner to select one for her at random. Use the list of different kinds of puppies available to determine the probability of each event. (*Hint*: Drawing a picture might help. Draw one on the back.)

| Puppies |
|---|
| 2 puppies with black stripes, both male |
| 3 tan puppies with white spots, 1 male, 2 female |
| 2 white puppies with black spots, both female |
| 1 black puppy, male |
| 1 white puppy, male |
| 1 tan puppy, female |

|  | Decimal | Percent |
|---|---|---|
| **5.** Gina receives an all-white puppy. | _____ | _____ |
| **6.** Gina receives a male puppy. | _____ | _____ |
| **7.** Gina receives a female spotted puppy. | _____ | _____ |
| **8.** Gina receives a female striped puppy. | _____ | _____ |
| **9.** Gina receives a white female puppy with black spots. | _____ | _____ |
| **10.** Gina receives a puppy without any black. | _____ | _____ |

Hal has gone fishing for the day. There are 7 carp (non-edible), 9 mackerel, 38 trout, and 46 catfish in the lake. Assume he catches one fish at random. While he is fishing, his son Peter goes diving for lost treasures. He reaches into the treasure chest and randomly chooses a coin. In the treasure chest, there are 16 tin, 12 titanium, 10 bronze, 8 copper, 3 silver, and 1 gold coins. Only the gold and titanium coins are still shiny. Only the gold, silver, copper, bronze, and titanium coins are valuable.

**Directions:** Use the information on how to show probability as a fraction, decimal, and percent on page 9 to help predict the outcomes below.

|  | Fraction | Decimal | Percent |
|---|---|---|---|
| **1.** Hal catches a catfish. | _____ | _____ | _____ |
| **2.** Hal catches a non-edible fish. | _____ | _____ | _____ |
| **3.** Hal catches a two-syllable fish. | _____ | _____ | _____ |
| **4.** Peter selects the gold coin. | _____ | _____ | _____ |
| **5.** Peter selects a valuable coin. | _____ | _____ | _____ |
| **6.** Peter selects a copper coin. | _____ | _____ | _____ |

**7.** Which fish is Hal least likely to catch?_____

**8.** Which coin is Peter most likely to grab?_____

## Facts to Know

When considering the likelihood and unlikelihood of an event, the sum of these two probabilities is 100% or 1.

### Example: Go Swimming

Ron estimates there is a 30% chance he will go swimming today.

The likelihood of this event occurring (30%) + the likelihood of this event not occurring ($x$) = 100%.

Therefore, the chance that Ron will not go swimming today is 70%.

**Compare:** The probability that Ron will swim is less than the probability that Ron will not swim.

### Example: Roll a Die

The probability of rolling a 6 = $\frac{1}{6}$

The probability of rolling a 1, 2, 3, 4, or 5 = $\frac{5}{6}$

The likelihood of rolling a 6 ($\frac{1}{6}$) + the likelihood of not rolling a 6 ($\frac{5}{6}$) = $\frac{6}{6}$ or 1

**Compare:** The probability of rolling a 6 is less than the probability of not rolling a 6.

## Compound Events

To find the probability of two events occurring at the same time, multiply the two numerical probabilities, draw a tree diagram, or make a list.

### Example: Do the Hokey Pokey

A class uses a spinner to determine what will "go in" the circle when playing the Hokey Pokey. One spinner is labeled "Right" and "Left." A second spinner has four body parts on it: hand, foot, ear, and hip. All the events on each spinner are equally likely. (No one space is larger than another.) Find the probability that the students in the circle will put in their right hand and then multiply.

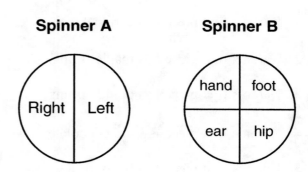

**Spinner A**

**Spinner B**

Spinner A lands on "right" = $\frac{1}{2}$

Spinner B lands on "hand" = $\frac{1}{4}$

→ $\frac{1}{2} \times \frac{1}{4} = \frac{1}{8}$ → right hand = $\frac{1}{8}$

# 3 ▶ Practice • • • • • • • • • • • • • Comparing Probabilities

The likelihood of an event + the unlikelihood of an event = 100% or 1.

- If the probability of spinning a 4 on a spinner is $\frac{1}{5}$, what is the probability of not spinning a 4? $\frac{1}{5} + x = \frac{5}{5}$ or 1, so $x = \frac{4}{5}$

- If the probability of spinning a 4 on a spinner is 20%, what is the probability of not spinning a 4? 20% + x = 100%, so x = 80%

- If the probability of spinning a 4 on a spinner is .2, what is the probability of not spinning a 4? .2 + x = 1.0, so x = .8

**Directions:** Karen has just opened a new box of chocolates. She doesn't know which kind of chocolate each candy is. She hopes to find a caramel or cherry first (her two favorites). Use the candy key to calculate the likelihood and unlikelihood of each event. Write the probabilities as a fraction (without reducing), decimal, or percent. Then compare the two outcomes using >, <, or =.

### Candy Key

maple =  solid chocolate =  

caramel =  orange =  

cherry =  

|  | probability of this event occurring | | probability of this event not occurring |
|---|---|---|---|
| 1. Karen's first piece is a caramel. | _____ | ◯ | _____ |
| 2. Karen's first piece has maple filling. | _____ | ◯ | _____ |
| 3. Karen's first piece has orange filling. | _____ | ◯ | _____ |
| 4. Karen's first piece is solid chocolate. | _____ | ◯ | _____ |
| 5. Karen's first piece has fruity filling. | _____ | ◯ | _____ |
| 6. Karen's first piece has chocolate coating. | _____ | ◯ | _____ |
| 7. Karen's first piece is a maple or caramel. | _____ | ◯ | _____ |
| 8. Karen's first piece has cherry filling. | _____ | ◯ | _____ |
| 9. Karen's first piece has a liquid center. | _____ | ◯ | _____ |
| 10. Karen's first piece is one of her favorites. | _____ | ◯ | _____ |

You can multiply to determine the total possible outcomes and the probability of a compound event.

---

**Example**

Two spinners have the colors black, blue, red, and orange in equal sections. What is the probability of spinning black on both spinners?

Multiply to find the total possible outcomes: 4 outcomes x 4 outcomes = 16

Multiply to find the probability: $\frac{1}{4}$ x $\frac{1}{4}$ = $\frac{1}{16}$

---

**Directions:** Multiply to find the total possible outcomes.

1. Janet has a choice of 7 flowers to plant in her garden. Each flower comes in 5 colors. How many total choices does she have? _____

2. Julia can earn an A, B, C, D, or F in her subjects. How many different outcomes are possible on her report card if she has 6 subjects? _____

3. Jared wants to choose a sport to play each day of the week. He has his choice of soccer, baseball, basketball, football, tennis, and hockey. How many possible combinations are there to choose from for a seven-day week? _____

4. A pet store has 20 cages available for each of the 20 different animals. How many ways might they organize their store? _____

**Directions:** Multiply to find the probability for each event. Write the probability as a fraction, decimal, or percent.

5. Mrs. Marsh gives homework on Tuesday. She may assign a task in either science, reading, math or social studies. What is the probability that she will assign math homework on Tuesday?

   _____

6. Mr. Jones wishes to buy a new vehicle. He has limited his choices to either a van, sports car, truck, station wagon, or convertible. Each vehicle comes in five colors: blue, red, black, yellow, and white. What is the probability he will choose a red station wagon?

   _____

7. Two children plan to use one of two diving boards at the pool, a low dive and a high dive. What is the probability that both children will choose the high-dive? _____

8. The Smith family has 3 children. Each child is allowed one pet. They may choose either a rabbit, dog, hamster, or cat. What is the probability that all three children will choose a cat? _____

9. Three children on the playground have their choice of 2 different colored balls to play with. What is the probability that all three children will select the same colored ball? _____

A tree diagram can help you show the possible outcomes of events.

The outcomes of rolling a 6 and then a 3 with one die.

The outcomes of flipping heads, then tails, then heads with one coin.

| Roll 1 | Roll 2 | Roll 1 | Roll 2 |
|---|---|---|---|
| 1 | 1 2 3 4 5 6 | 4 | 1 2 3 4 5 6 |
| 2 | 1 2 3 4 5 6 | 5 | 1 2 3 4 5 6 |
| 3 | 1 2 3 4 5 6 | 6 | 1 2 ③ 4 5 6 |

1 outcome out of 8 possibilities

1 outcome out of 36 possibilities

| Outcome | Flip 1 | Flip 2 | Flip 3 |
|---|---|---|---|
| 1 | H | H | H |
| 2 | H | T | T |
| 3 | H | T | H |
| 4 | H | H | T |
| 5 | T | T | T |
| 6 | T | H | H |
| 7 | T | H | T |
| 8 | T | T | H |

**Directions:** Use a tree diagram or make a list of the outcomes for the following situations to help you answer the following questions.

> Mark is using a spinner for an activity. The spinner is equally divided into two sections, one labeled "In" and the other labeled "Out." He must spin the spinner three times in a row.

1. How many possible outcomes are there for this activity?_____

2. What is the probability that the spinner will land on "In" twice and "Out" once? _____

> Eric is playing a cube game with two cubes. the vowel cube has the letters A, E, I, O, U, and Y. The consonant cube has the letters B, D, H, S, T, and G. He needs to roll each cube once to see if he can make a word.

3. How many possible outcomes are there for this game? _____

4. How many of these outcomes are actual words? List them. _____

_____

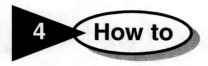

## Facts to Know

### Making Predictions with Probability

Analyzing the likelihood of outcomes can help you make predictions and, consequently, decisions regarding your interest or involvement in a situation.

Your mom allowed you $5.00 towards playing games at the local fair. You want to use your money wisely and have decided on four games to choose from. Analyzing the probability of winning each game and considering its cost-effectiveness may help you make better decisions as to how to spend your $5.00.

### Probability of Wins Based on Saturday's Outcomes

| Game | Probability of Winning | Cost to Play |
|---|---|---|
| Water Pistol Target Shooting | 25% | $0.50 |
| Ring Toss | 10% | $0.25 |
| Balloon Popping | 42% | $1.00 |
| Hoops | 58% | $2.00 |

### What Does the Data Tell You?

- The Ring Toss has the lowest probability of wins, but it also costs the least. You can expect to pay $2.50 to win at the Ring Toss.
- The Water Pistol game is more cost effective than the Ring Toss. You can expect to pay $2.00 before winning this game.
- You have a better likelihood of winning the Balloon Popping game, but can expect to pay about as much to win as the Water Pistol game.
- Hoops has the best chance to win, but you can expect to pay about $4.00 to win once.

Using the information you have gathered by analyzing the probability of winning each game along with its cost-effectiveness, you decide to play both the Water Pistol game and the Ring Toss.

### Making Predictions with Data

A collection of data can help people make predictions and, therefore, make more educated decisions.

What if you are a jeweler looking for a location to open a new store? You have three sites in mind and guess that the best success will be on the busiest street. Data siting the number of cars that pass by during certain hours of the day may help you make your decision as to where to place your store.

### Average Number of Cars that Pass by the Potential Store Location on Any Weekday

| Time | Street 1 | Street 2 | Street 3 |
|---|---|---|---|
| 8:00 A.M. – 10:00 A.M. | 17 | 35 | 25 |
| 10:00 A.M. – 12:00 P.M. | 6 | 16 | 25 |
| 12:00 P.M. – 2:00 P.M. | 12 | 27 | 10 |
| 2:00 P.M. – 4:00 P.M. | 9 | 20 | 8 |
| 4:00 P.M. – 6:00 P.M. | 20 | 42 | 48 |

### What Does the Data Tell You?

- Street 1, compared to Streets 2 and 3, is rather slow.
- Street 2 has the highest total cars pass by on average.
- Street 3 is pretty busy, too, but mostly in the morning and late afternoon.

If you plan to run your business from 9:00 A.M. until 5:00 P.M., Street 2 is probably the best location for your store. You can expect a constant flow of traffic all day long.

You have just cleaned out your closet and have decided upon some toys to sell. You are thinking about taking them to a local consignment shop where someone will sell them for you. You wish to earn the highest profit possible.

### Consignment Dealer Records

| Consignment Shop | % Merchandise Sold | Profit to Store | Profit to You |
|---|---|---|---|
| Amy's Afterthoughts | 55% | 50% | 50% |
| Jerry's Junk House | 12% | 30% | 70% |
| Ronnie's Relics | 75% | 80% | 20% |
| Sarah's Sellables | 42% | 50% | 50% |

## Table Information

"% Merchandise Sold" indicates the percentage, on average, of merchandise sold per week.

"Profit to Store" is the percent of the sale the store keeps.

"Profit to You" is the percent of the sale that you get to keep.

## How to Calculate Profit

Each percent converts to pennies on the dollar. A 60% "Profit to Store" means the storeowner keeps 60 cents of every dollar sold. This leaves 40 cents, or 40% for the person who brought in the merchandise (you).

> **Example:** With an item that sells for $5.00, the storeowner keeps 60% of the $5.00.
>
> 60% x $5.00 = $3.00. You would receive $2.00.

**Directions:** Use the table above to answer the questions below.

1. Which store has the highest probability of selling your toys? _____

2. Which store has the highest profit going to the person who brings in the merchandise?

   _____

3. With which two shops would you have a nearly equal chance of selling your merchandise as well as receiving a similar profit? _____

4. Compare the advantages and disadvantages of taking your toys to Jerry's Junk House.

   _____

5. You think your toys will sell for about $5.00 total. To which shop will you bring them? Why?

   _____

   _____

You and your family wish to plan a winter and a summer vacation. You look forward to skiing, sledding, skating, and warming your feet by an indoor fire during your winter trip. Swimming, boating, biking, and roasting marshmallows by the campfire is what you look forward to during your summer trip.

## Climate and Precipitation Data from Around the United States

| City | Average High/Low (in °F) | | Average Precipitation (snow or rain, in inches) | | Average Number of Snow or Rain Days | |
|---|---|---|---|---|---|---|
| | January | July | January | July | January | July |
| Anchorage, AK | 21/8 | 65/52 | 0.79 | 1.71 | 8 | 12 |
| Burlington, VT | 25/8 | 81/60 | 1.82 | 3.65 | 14 | 12 |
| Chicago, IL | 29/13 | 84/63 | 1.53 | 3.66 | 11 | 10 |
| Denver, CO | 43/16 | 88/59 | 0.50 | 1.91 | 6 | 9 |
| Houston, TX | 61/40 | 93/72 | 3.29 | 3.29 | 11 | 10 |
| Washington, D.C. | 42/27 | 89/71 | 2.70 | 3.80 | 10 | 10 |

**Directions:** Use the data from the chart above to answer the following questions.

1. In which city would you have the least probability of being rained out in July?

   _____

2. What can you say about the amount of rainfall in July in Houston compared to that in Denver?

   _____

3. Describe how you might pack differently if you plan to camp in Anchorage in July compared to camping in Washington, D.C. in July. _____

   _____

4. Which city do you think would make the best location for your family's summer vacation? Why? _____

   _____

5. In which city would you have the least probability of being snowed (or rained) out in January?

   _____

6. Based on the daily average temperature, which city has the least probability of snow in January?

   _____

7. How does the January snowfall/rainfall in Burlington compare to that in Chicago? _____

   _____

8. Which city do you think would make the best location for your family's winter vacation? Why? _____

   _____

**Directions:** Use the data from the graphs below to answer the questions that follow.

Hillary is very proud of herself when she wins the electronic game that she plays. The line graph below shows her progress as she plays the game again and again.

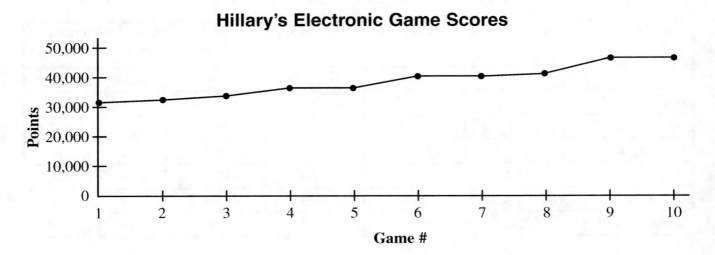

**Hillary's Electronic Game Scores**

1. How do Hillary's scores compare from game to game? _____

2. Would Hillary's score be likely or unlikely to go up in the next game?_____

3. What numerical value would you give to the probability that Hillary will score over 20,000 points during her next play? _____

Mrs. Johnson's class is on a nature hike at school. She shared a graph with her students that her previous class had made.

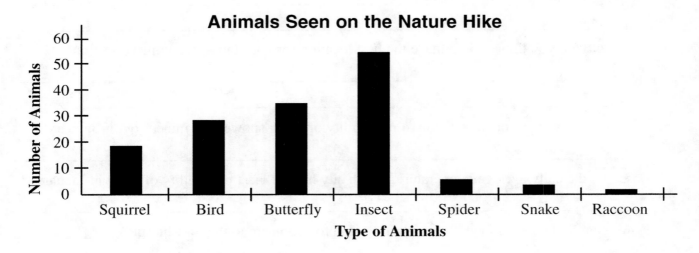

**Animals Seen on the Nature Hike**

4. Using the information from the above graph, which animal can Mrs. Johnson's class expect to see the most of? _____

5. What numerical value would you give to the probability that the class will see a snake?

_____

## Facts to Know

A **ratio** compares two numbers, groups, or quantities. The ratios below compare the circles, squares, and shapes.

### Writing Ratios

Compare these two ratios. Although they are similar, they do not express the same comparison.

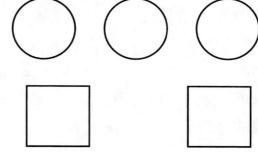

    The ratio of circles to squares is 3:2.

    The ratio of squares to circles is 2:3.

Compare these two ratios. They also are similar, but express two very different ratios.

    The ratio of circles to shapes is 3:5.

    The ratio of shapes to circles is 5:3.

A ratio may be written in three ways. The first ratio comparing circles to squares may be written as 3:2, 3 to 2, or $\frac{3}{2}$.

### Equivalent Ratios

Ratios may be enlarged or reduced, multiplied to show larger quantities, and divided to show smaller quantities. Use a chart to help organize the information.

    **Example:** The latest poll shows that people prefer dogs as pets, 3 to 1, over cats. What would this mean statistically if 21 people preferred dogs?

| Dogs | 3 | 6 | 9 | 12 | 15 | 18 | 21 |
|------|---|---|---|----|----|----|----|
| Cats | 1 | 2 | 3 | 4 | 5 | 6 | 7 |

The equivalent ratio indicates that 7 people would prefer cats.

    **Example:** On a busy highway, you might see 50 trucks to every 200 cars. What if 100 cars were on the road? What if 20 cars were on the road? What if 4 cars were on the road?

| Cars | 200 | 100 | 20 | 4 |
|------|-----|-----|----|----|
| Trucks | 50 | 25 | 5 | 1 |

### Ratios as Odds

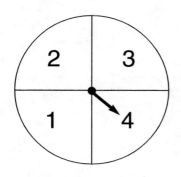

Ratios can be used to show probability, too. Look at this spinner. You can write the odds for or against spinning a 4 as a ratio.

Odds **for** spinning a 4 are 1 to 3 (or 1:3).

Odds **against** spinning a 4 are 3 to 1 (or 3:1).

Compare this with the probability of spinning a 2 as 1 in 2 or $\frac{1}{2}$ or 1: 2.

**Directions:** A ratio can be written as 3:2, 3 to 2, or $\frac{3}{2}$. Write each ratio in three ways. The first one has been done for you.

Carlos had 5 quarters, 6 dimes, 3 nickels, and 8 pennies in his pocket.

| | | | $\frac{8}{3}$ |
|---|---|---|---|
| 1. pennies to nickels | 8:3 | 8 to 3 | |
| 2. quarters to dimes | | | |
| 3. quarters to coins | | | |
| 4. coins to quarters | | | |
| 5. dimes to pennies | | | |
| 6. quarters to pennies | | | |
| 7. nickels to pennies | | | |

A pet store has 12 puppies, 15 dogs, 10 kittens, 10 cats, and 50 fish.

| | | | |
|---|---|---|---|
| 8. puppies to dogs | | | |
| 9. dogs to puppies | | | |
| 10. cats to kittens | | | |
| 11. fish to dogs | | | |
| 12. pets to fish | | | |
| 13. cats to pets | | | |
| 14. kittens to cats | | | |
| 15. hamsters to kittens | | | |

**In Your Own Words**

**Directions:** Write three different ratios to compare different objects in your classroom.

(For example, students to desks, coats to desks, or students wearing jeans to students wearing dresses.)

_____

_____

_____

_____

_____

A local candy shop has the following items for sale.

| | |
|---|---|
| 18 lollipops | 15 rock candies |
| 8 cotton candies | 6 kinds of fudge |
| 24 boxes of chewy candies | 16 choices of "candies by the ounce" |
| 24 boxes of chocolate | 9 kinds of candy sticks |

**Directions:** For each question write solutions to compare the following ratios.

**1.** Which kinds of candy have a 1:1 ratio?

_____

**2.** Which kinds of candy have a 3:1 ratio?

_____

**3.** Which kinds of candy have a 5:3 ratio?

_____

**4.** Which kinds of candy have a 30:45 ratio?

_____

**5.** Which kinds of candy have a 30:36 ratio?

_____

**6.** Which kinds of candy have a 32:24 ratio?

_____

An advertiser has made the following claims for some of its products.

> 3 out of 5 people prefer ZAX gum.
> Blotus Bubbles are preferred 5:1.
> Omega Bank is preferred 2:1.
> 2 out of 3 teachers prefer Write-on Chalk.

**7.** What is the minimum number of people surveyed according to the ZAX gum claim?_____

**8.** If 50 people prefer Omega Bank, statistically how many people don't prefer it? _____

**9.** If 5 people don't prefer Blotus Bubbles, how many people do prefer them?_____

**10.** If 300 teachers were polled, statistically how many prefer Write-on Chalk?_____

Angela likes to play card games that are predictable. Sometimes she tests the odds of selecting certain cards from the deck.

What you need to know about a standard deck of cards.

- There are 52 cards altogether.

- There are 4 suits of cards. Hearts and diamonds are red. Spades and clubs are black.

- In each suit there are 13 cards: ace, 2, 3, 4, 5, 6, 7, 8, 9, 10, jack, queen, and king.

**Directions:** Use the information you learned on page 21 that tells how to use ratios to show odds. Write the odds for each event as a ratio.

What are the odds **for** Angela selecting these cards at random?

What are the odds **against** Angela selecting these cards at random?

**1.** a red card _____

**2.** a black card _____

**3.** a heart_____

**4.** an odd-numbered spade _____

**5.** a jack, queen, or king of any suit?_____

**6.** an ace of any suit_____

**7.** an even card of any suit_____

**8.** an even red card_____

**9.** yellow card of any suit _____

**10.** a spade _____

## Facts to Know

### Example

You and a friend roll a pair of dice. You score 1 point if the total turns up odd. Your friend scores 1 point if the total turns up even. Is this fair?

Chart the outcomes to find out.

| | | |
|---|---|---|
| **Dice Totals** | *Odd*: 1, 3, 5, 7, 9, 11 | *Even*: 2, 4, 6, 8, 10, 12 |
| **Probability** | *Rolling Odd*: $\frac{6}{12}$ | *Rolling Even*: $\frac{6}{12}$ |
| **Ratio of** | *Odd to Even*: 6:6 | |

Since the outcomes for both players are equally likely, yes, this is a fair game.

### Example

What if you score 1 point if the total is a multiple of 3 and your friend scores 1 point for all other totals? Is the game still fair?

Chart the outcomes to find out.

| | | |
|---|---|---|
| **Dice Totals** | *Multiple of 3*: 3, 6, 9, 12 | *All other totals*: 1, 2, 4, 5, 7, 8, 10, 11 |
| **Probability** | *Rolling a multiple of 3*: $\frac{4}{12}$ | *Rolling another total*: $\frac{8}{12}$ |
| **Ratio of** | *Multiples of 3 to Not Multiples of 3*: 4:8 | |

Your friend is twice as likely to score a point. No, this game is not fair. The game could be made fair if you scored 2 points for your wins while your friend only scored 1 point.

### Example

A chart, diagram, or graph may help you analyze outcomes to check for fairness. Do these outcomes seem fair?

**Percent of Wins for the Game "Sticks"**

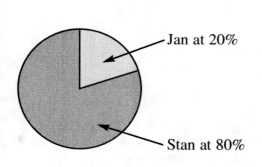

**Outcomes of Flipping a Coin Three Times**

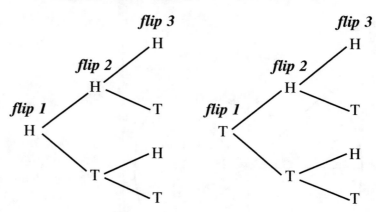

## Discussion Questions:

Would you play sticks if you were Jan? Why or why not? If one person scores one point if the coins come up the same, and another person scores one point if the coins come up different, is this game fair? Explain. What could make the game fair?

**Directions:** Use the information on page 25 to determine whether or not the outcomes have equal ratios. Then, decide whether the situations are fair or not.

Donna and Jessica have 9 colored candies in a bag. 4 candies are blue, 4 candies are green, and 1 piece of candy is yellow. Each girl gets to pull out one piece of candy, then put it back. Donna scores a point if the piece of candy is blue. Jessica scores a point if the piece of candy is green.

1. Ratio of blue to green candies _____
2. Ratio of blue candies to all candy _____
3. Ratio of green to blue candies _____
4. Ratio of green candies to all candy _____
5. Is this a fair game? Explain. _____
_____

Donna and Jessica's friend Melanie comes to play, too. She scores a point each time she pulls out a yellow piece of candy.

6. Ratio of yellow to green candies _____
7. Ratio of yellow candy to all candy _____
8. Ratio of yellow to blue candies _____
9. Is this fair? Explain. _____
_____

10. How many turns to every 1 turn of Donna and Jessica's would improve Melanie's odds and make the ratios equally likely? _____

11. Look at the pie chart to the right. Do the outcomes of this game seem fair? Why or why not? _____
_____
_____

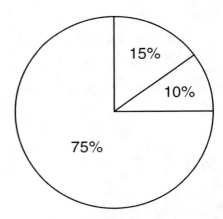

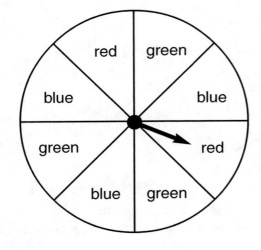

12. Look at the spinner to the left. Write the ratios for spinning each color. If your chances of winning a game were determined by the color of your spin, which color would you choose and why? _____
_____
_____

**Directions:** Make a chart to analyze the outcomes. Use the information on page 25 to determine whether or not the outcomes have equal ratios. Decide whether the situations are fair or not.

John and Garrett play a dice game. They each roll two dice and multiply the numbers. John scores 1 point if the product is even. Garrett scores 1 point if the product is odd.

**1.** Complete the chart below to observe the outcomes.

| X | 1 | 2 | 3 | 4 | 5 | 6 |
|---|---|---|---|---|---|---|
| 1 |   |   |   |   | 5 |   |
| 2 |   |   | 6 |   |   | 12 |
| 3 | 3 |   |   |   |   |   |
| 4 |   | 8 |   |   |   |   |
| 5 |   |   |   | 20 |   |   |
| 6 |   |   | 18 |   |   |   |

**2.** What is the ratio of even products to total products?_____

**3.** What is the ratio of odd products to total products?_____

**4.** What is the ratio of even products to odd products? _____

**5.** Is this a fair game?  *Yes   No*

Explain._____

_____

_____

_____

Bob and Todd try this game. Each player flips three pennies at the same time. If Bob flips and all three coins come up either all heads or all tails, he scores three points. If Todd flips them and the three coins come up different, he scores one point.

**6.** Finish the tree diagram to show all the outcomes.

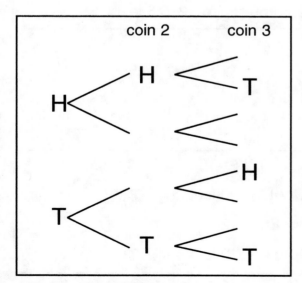

**7.** What is the ratio of all heads to total outcomes?

_____

**8.** What is the ratio of all tails to total outcomes?

_____

**9.** What is the ratio of all heads or all tails to not all heads or all tails? _____

**10.** Is this game fair?  *Yes   No*

Explain. _____

_____

**Ratios** may be used to show similar figures. When planning a large building or other structure, a scale model is usually drawn or constructed first. Hobby trains, too, are created to scale. A chart will help identify the dimensions of the scale. Here's how.

**Example:** An architect designs a model of his bridge. The scale is 100:1.

Here's a chart following the ratios of the bridge's dimensions.

|  | Bridge | Model |
|---|---|---|
| **Height** | 200 feet | 2 feet |
| **Length** | 100 feet | 1 foot |
| **Width** | 75 feet | .75 feet (8 in.) |

**Directions:** Use the charts below to help identify the specific scales.

|  | Spacecraft | Model |
|---|---|---|
| **Height** | 50 meters | 5 cm |
| **Length** | 150 meters | 15 cm |
| **Width** | 50 meters | 5 cm |

A scientist creates a scale model of a new spacecraft. The chart on the left shows his model's dimensions.

1. What is the scale?
   _____

(*Hint*: 1 meter = 100 centimeters)

A high school student constructs a model rocket. The ratio of a real rocket to this model rocket is 100:1.

Complete the chart on the right to show all of the dimensions.

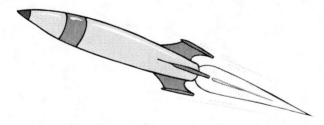

|  | Rocket | Model |
|---|---|---|
| **Height** | 75 feet | 2. _____ |
| **Length** | 3. | 3.5 feet |
| **Width** | 4. | 0.75 feet |
| **Circumference** | 235.5 feet | 5. _____ |

Based on her drawings, Glenda Persham won a contest to design a statue for the new town square. Now she needs to create a model of the actual statue. Using the dimensions of the statue, determine a good scale Glenda could use.

Complete the chart to show her model's dimensions.

6. Scale for statue model: _____
   (*Hint*: 1 foot = 12 inches)

|  | Statue | Model |
|---|---|---|
| **Height** | 20 feet | 7. _____ |
| **Length** | 12 feet | 8. _____ |
| **Width** | 10 feet | 9. _____ |

## Facts to Know

### Calculating the Mean

The **mean** tells the **average** number of items for a group. Suppose three people ate jellybeans. One person had 8, a second person had 4, and a third had 9. On average, how many jellybeans did each person eat?

| To calculate the mean |
| --- |
| **1.** Add the jellybeans eaten. |
| **2.** Divide by the number of people. |

**Example**

1. Add the jellybeans eaten.

   **8 + 4 + 9 = 21**

2. Divide by the number of people.

   **21 ÷ 3 = 7**

   The **mean** number of jellybeans each person ate is 7.

### Finding the Range

The **range** in a set of data is the difference between the greatest and the least value . This information will help you set up a graph for any set of data.

| To calculate the range |
| --- |
| **1.** Subtract the lowest number in a data set from the highest. |

**Example**

1. Subtract the lowest number of jellybeans from the highest.

   **9 − 4 = 5**

2. The **range** of jellybeans eaten is 5.

### Charting the Data

Let's expand the example above to include a whole class. Of the 25 people who ate jellybeans, five people had 8 jellybeans, five people had 7 jellybeans, five people had 6 jellybeans, one person had 9 jellybeans, and nine people had 4 jellybeans.

Calculate the **mean**.

1. Add to find how many jellybeans were eaten in all.

   **40 + 35 + 30 + 9 + 36 = 150**

2. Divide by the total number of people.

   **150 ÷ 25 = 6**

Calculate the **range**.

1. Subtract the lowest number of jellybeans eaten from the highest (9 − 4 = 5).

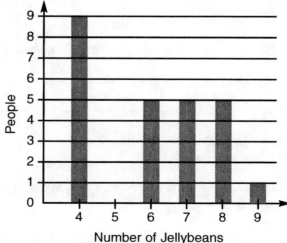

A **bar graph** helps organize the data. Look at the bar graph above. The range of jellybeans eaten (from 4 to 9) is shown on the horizontal axis. The number of people is shown on the vertical axis. The length of each bar represents the number of people that ate a certain amount of jellybeans.

**Directions:** Use the information you learned on page 29 to find the mean, or average, for each set of data.

1. 7, 2, 6, 5          Mean_____
2. 9, 4, 1, 3, 8       Mean_____
3. 16, 14, 11, 15      Mean_____
4. 25, 25, 25, 25      Mean_____
5. 33, 18, 40, 21, 13  Mean_____

6. 57, 28, 86          Mean_____
7. 92, 43, 75, 30      Mean_____
8. 133, 122, 144       Mean_____
9. 521, 368, 860       Mean_____
10. 1,001, 1,002, 1,003  Mean_____

11. Look at the totals above. Which sets of date above have the same mean? Explain how different sets of data can have the same mean. _____

_____

_____

Bob wishes to find out how well he is doing in math class. He asks Mr. Giles for his grade. Mr. Giles only gives Bob a set of numbers from his grade book and explains that his current grade is the mean of these. Help Bob find his grade.

| Grading Scale | |
|---|---|
| 94 – 100 | A |
| 85 – 93 | B |
| 78 – 84 | C |
| 70 – 77 | D |
| 0 – 69 | F |

**Bob's Grades**

*test scores*: 95, 92, 88
*quiz scores*: 85, 85, 91, 100
*class work*: 88, 86, 90, 98, 94

12. Estimate first. Looking at all the grades, what mean grade do you think Bob has earned so far?

_____

13. Now calculate the mean. _____

14. Look at the grading scale. What grade has Bob earned so far? _____

15. Do you think this grade is a fair average for Bob?   *Yes*   *No*   Explain your answer._____

_____

After seeing Bob with his class average, Brenda is interested in her own grade. She, too, asks Mr. Giles for her grades.

16. Do you think Brenda's class average will be similar to Bob's?   *Yes*   *No*

17. Calculate Brenda's mean grade. _____

18. What is her letter grade? _____

**Brenda's Grades**

*test scores*: 89, 92, 86
*quiz scores*: 78, 82, 85, 90
*class work*: 90, 90, 86, 100, 100

**Directions:** Use the information you learned on page 29 to find the range for each set of data. Then make a bar graph for each data set.

Mrs. Ikeman's class conducted a study to see how many hours each student spends watching television each week. The students discovered the following information.

| # of Hours | # of Students | Bar Graph of Data |
|------------|---------------|-------------------|
| 10 | 6 | |
| 12 | 4 | |
| 15 | 7 | |
| 16 | 3 | |
| 18 | 3 | |
| 19 | 2 | |
| 20 | 1 | |

1. Range of hours spent watching television: _____

Lonnie helped his gym teacher organize his class' sit-up information. Each student did as many sit-ups as he or she could in one minute. Lonnie's gym teacher gave him the following data.

| # of Sit-ups | # of Students | Bar Graph of Data |
|--------------|---------------|-------------------|
| 31 | 1 | |
| 38 | 8 | |
| 39 | 7 | |
| 40 | 6 | |
| 42 | 5 | |
| 43 | 2 | |

2. Range of sit-ups in one minute: _____

Sarah and her friends had a contest to see how many times they could skip rocks across the pond. She and two friends each skipped 10 rocks. They counted the skips for each throw. This is what they counted.

| # of Skips | # of Times | Bar Graph of Data |
|------------|------------|-------------------|
| 1 | 4 | |
| 2 | 8 | |
| 3 | 9 | |
| 4 | 3 | |
| 5 | 3 | |
| 6 | 2 | |
| 8 | 1 | |

3. Range of skips: _____

You may wish to estimate the mean or range for some sets of data. For example, if you wish to purchase a new television set, you may get three prices and estimate their totals so you know about what to expect to pay.

Let's say you look through the ads and find three similar sets. Their prices are $138.98, $149.96, and $150.99. By estimating their prices at $140, $150, and $150, you can quickly determine that you might expect to pay between $140 and $150 (the range) for a new television set.

If you wished to estimate how much homework you receive each week, you might estimate your weekly homework load for one month, then estimate the average. You estimate 3 hours the first week, 4 hours the second week, 5 hours the third week, and 2 hours the fourth week. Looking at these numbers, and without computing the actual mean, you can estimate that you receive between 3 and 4 hours of homework each week.

**Directions:** Use the chart below to answer the following questions.

These cities receive the following precipitation amounts, on average, each month. (All values are in inches.)

|  | J | F | M | A | M | J | J | A | S | O | N | D |
|---|---|---|---|---|---|---|---|---|---|---|---|---|
| **Honolulu, HI** | 3.6 | 2.2 | 2.2 | 1.5 | 1.1 | 0.5 | 0.6 | 0.4 | 0.8 | 2.3 | 3 | 3.8 |
| **Baltimore, MD** | 3.1 | 3.1 | 3.4 | 3.1 | 3.7 | 3.7 | 3.7 | 3.9 | 3.4 | 3 | 3.3 | 3.4 |
| **Nashville, TN** | 3.6 | 3.8 | 4.9 | 4.4 | 4.9 | 3.6 | 4 | 3.5 | 3.5 | 2.6 | 4.1 | 4.6 |
| **Reno, NV** | 1.1 | 1 | 0.7 | 0.4 | 0.7 | 0.5 | 0.3 | 0.3 | 0.4 | 0.4 | 0.9 | 1 |
| **Tampa, FL** | 2 | 3.1 | 3 | 1.2 | 3.1 | 5.5 | 6.6 | 7.6 | 6 | 2 | 1.8 | 2.2 |

1. Estimate which city receives the most precipitation, on average, each year. _____

2. Estimate which city receives the least amount of precipitation, on average, each year.

    _____

3. Estimate which cities have about equal amounts of annual rainfall. _____

    _____

4. About how much rain, in whole inches, does Baltimore receive in one year?_____

5. About how much rain, in whole inches, does Reno receive in one year?_____

6. About how much rain, in whole inches, does Honolulu receive in one year? _____

7. On average, about how much rain does Baltimore receive each month? _____

8. On average, about how much rain does Tampa receive each month?_____

9. On average, about how much rain does Reno receive each month?_____

10. What is the range of monthly precipitation for the five cities?_____

## Facts to Know

The **median** is another way to show an average. It is the middle number in a set of data. Suppose you wished to find the median weight of all the dogs weighed at the vet's office for one day. Look at this data.

### Example

Dog weights for one day (in lbs.): 75, 32, 15, 8, 78, 123, 48, 55, 72, 43, 78, 21, 130

To find the median:

**1.** Arrange the data from least to greatest. **2.** Find the middle number.

▼

**dog weights:** 8, 15, 21, 32, 43, 48, 55, 72, 75, 78, 78, 123, 130

The median weight of the dogs is 55 lbs.

*Note: For data sets with an even number of data, add the two middle numbers and divide by 2.*

### Example

The vet weighed 12 cats. Their weights (in lbs.) are listed in the chart.

▼

**Step 1:** 8, 9, 9, 10, 10, 10, 11, 11, 12, 12, 12, 14

**Step 2:** 10 + 11 = 21  21 ÷ 2 = 10.5 lbs.

The median weight of the cats is 10.5 lbs.

| cat weights | | |
|---|---|---|
| 10 | 10 | 9 |
| 14 | 11 | 12 |
| 8 | 12 | 11 |
| 12 | 10 | 9 |

The **mode** is another way to express an average. This is the number in a set of data that occurs more often than any other number.

Look at this data.

| Populations of 10 Counties in Montana (rounded to the nearest hundred) | | | |
|---|---|---|---|
| Beaverhead | 8,800 | Madison | 6,400 |
| Carbon | 8,900 | Park | 15,700 |
| Dawson | 9,000 | Prairie | 1,300 |
| Flathead | 67,300 | Rosebud | 10,800 |
| Lake | 23,700 | Treasure | 900 |

None of the data occurs more than once. There is no mode for this set of data.

*Note: The mode is not zero (0). A mode of zero (0) indicates that zero is part of the data set and occurs the most frequently.*

Likewise, a set of data may have more than one mode. In the cat data set above, there are two modes, 10 and 12. Both of these numbers occur three times.

**Directions:** Use the information on page 33 to find the median and mode for each set of data.

1. 6, 12, 3, 15, 3, 9, 2, 8, 1          median _____          mode _____

2. 94, 67, 68, 30, 91, 94, 95          median _____          mode _____

3. 771, 786, 745, 770, 786, 790, 786          median _____          mode _____

4. $19, $24, $30, $30, $19, $28          median _____          mode _____

| Ron's Sticker Collection | |
| --- | --- |
| stars | 36 |
| happy faces | 41 |
| animals | 40 |
| cartoon characters | 40 |
| plants | 35 |

5. What is the median number of stickers Ron has? _____

6. What is the mode number of stickers Ron has? _____

Gerry shops for new school clothes. He spends $35, $38, and $40 on pants; $15, $28, and $20 on shirts; $15 on socks; $68 and $35 on shoes.

7. What is the median amount of money Gerry spends on clothes? _____

8. What is the mode amount of money Gerry spends on clothes? _____

Henry's father wishes to buy a new car. He decides to compare gas mileage for five vehicles that he is considering.

| Miles Per Gallon (mpg) | | |
| --- | --- | --- |
| car | city | highway |
| sports car | 28 | 37 |
| family sedan | 25 | 32 |
| minivan | 22 | 28 |
| sports utility vehicle | 15 | 21 |
| small car | 25 | 37 |

9. What is the median city mileage?

_____

10. What is the median highway mileage? _____

11. What is the mode city mileage?

_____

12. What is the mode highway mileage?

_____

13. Which average, the median or mode, is a better average to represent the city mileage? _____

14. Which average, the median or mode, is a better average to represent the highway mileage?

_____

**Directions:** Use the graph as your source for data. Then, use what you learned on page 33 to find the median and mode for each set of data.

Fourth and fifth graders read books as part of their reading program. The number of books each class reads in one week was totaled and graphed below.

### Books Read by A Class for One Week

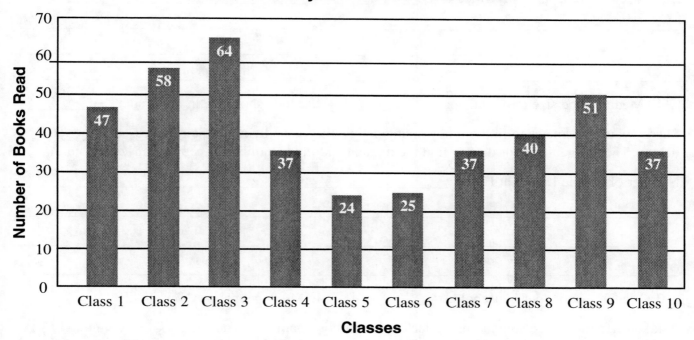

1. What is the mode number of books read by the fourth and fifth graders? _____

2. What is the median number of books read by the fourth and fifth graders? _____

For each book read, students took a test. The results of their tests are seen below as percentages.

**Hint:** To find the number of tests for each score, multiply the number of tests taken by the percentage.

Scored 100: 30%

Scored 80: 30%

Scored 60: 20%

Scored 40: 10%

Scored 20: 5%

Scored 0: 5%

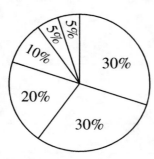

3. What percentage of students score 80% or 100%? _____

4. Based on the percentages, if 100 tests were taken, how many students would score 60%? _____

5. Based on the percentages, if 500 tests were taken, how many students would score 80% or 100%? _____

6. What is the median score? _____

7. What is the mode score? _____

**Directions:** Conduct these experiments to collect data. Then use what you learned on page 33 to find the median and mode for each set of data you collect.

Survey some classmates in your grade level to find out their shoe sizes. List each shoe size below. (If a person has a half size, round up to the next size.) Then, organize your data to find the median and mode for shoe sizes of students in your grade level.

Shoe sizes of students in my grade level:_____

_____

_____

_____

**1.** Median shoe size in my grade: _____     **2.** Mode shoe size in my grade: _____

Survey your classmates to find out how many people they have living in their homes. List the totals below. Then, organize your data to find the median and mode number of people per household.

Number of People Living at Home: _____

_____

_____

_____

**3.** Median people per household: _____     **4.** Mode people per household: _____

Ask some friends to do some jumping jacks. Count how many they can each do in one minute. List the number of jumping jacks your friends can do in one minute on the lines below. Then find the median and mode.

Number of Jumping Jacks in One Minute: _____

_____

_____

_____

**5.** Median jumping jacks in one minute: _____     **6.** Mode jumping jacks in one minute: _____

Conduct the same experiment above for skipping rope.

Number of rope skips in one minute:_____

_____

_____

_____

**7.** Median rope skips in one minute: _____     **8.** Mode rope skips in one minute:_____

## Facts to Know

### Stem-and-Leaf Plot

A **stem-and-leaf plot** may help you organize large sets of data to easily find the median and mode. To make a stem-and-leaf graph, list digits in the tens and higher place values in the stem. List the digits in the ones place value for each data in the leaf. For the number 72, the 7 is the stem and the 2 is the leaf. For the number 690, the 69 is the stem and the 0 is the leaf.

| Birds at the Aviary | | | |
|---|---|---|---|
| Robins | 131 | Finches | 132 |
| Blue Jays | 135 | Parrots | 141 |
| Cardinals | 132 | Toucans | 135 |
| Sparrows | 155 | Wrens | 138 |
| Peacocks | 133 | Woodpeckers | 138 |
| Canaries | 132 | Swallows | 150 |

**Example**

Listed are the numbers of various birds at the aviary. To find the median and mode, organize the data in a stem-and-leaf plot. Put the *tens* and *hundreds* in the stem. List the *ones,* in order, in the leaf.

| Stem | Leaf |
|---|---|
| 13 | 1 **2 2 2** 3 5 5 8 8 |
| 14 | 1 |
| 15 | 0 5 |

Now find the middle number to show the median. There are 12 quantities so the middle falls between the sixth and seventh numbers. Since there is an even number of data, add the two numbers together (135 + 135 = 270) and divide by 2 so 270 ÷ 2 = 135.

To find the mode, scan the leaves to determine which number occurs most frequently (132).

### Frequency Chart

Another way to quickly represent large sets of data is with a **frequency chart**. To make a frequency chart, tally each quantity in a set of data.

**Example:** The chart below shows the number of state representatives each state has in the House of Representatives. To make a frequency chart for the data, list the numbers from least to greatest, then tally the number of states with those quantities.

| AL | 7 | HA | 2 | MA | 10 | NM | 3 | SD | 1 |
|---|---|---|---|---|---|---|---|---|---|
| AK | 1 | ID | 2 | MI | 16 | NY | 31 | TN | 9 |
| AZ | 6 | IL | 20 | MN | 8 | NC | 12 | TX | 30 |
| AR | 4 | IN | 10 | MS | 5 | ND | 1 | UT | 3 |
| CA | 52 | IA | 5 | MO | 9 | OH | 19 | VT | 1 |
| CO | 6 | KS | 4 | MT | 1 | OK | 6 | VA | 11 |
| CT | 6 | KY | 6 | NE | 3 | OR | 5 | WA | 9 |
| DE | 1 | LA | 7 | NV | 2 | PA | 21 | WV | 3 |
| FL | 23 | ME | 2 | NH | 2 | RI | 2 | WI | 9 |
| GA | 11 | MD | 8 | NJ | 13 | SC | 6 | WY | 1 |

**Frequency Chart for State Representatives**

| | | | |
|---|---|---|---|
| 1– | ☒☒ II | 12– | I |
| 2– | ☒☒ I | 13– | I |
| 3– | IIII | 16– | I |
| 4– | II | 19– | I |
| 5– | III | 20– | I |
| 6– | ☒☒ I | 21– | I |
| 7– | II | 23– | I |
| 8– | II | 30– | I |
| 9– | IIII | 31– | I |
| 10– | II | 52– | I |
| 11– | II | | |

Now you can easily calculate that the median number of representatives is 6 and the mode is 1.

**Directions:** Use what you learned on page 37 to answer the questions below.

### Rhonda's Garden Plan

| | |
|---|---|
| beans – 12 | celery – 16 |
| carrots – 20 | cherry tomatoes – 18 |
| lettuce – 18 | brussels sprouts – 8 |
| tomatoes – 16 | potatoes – 20 |
| cucumbers – 20 | leeks – 16 |
| radishes – 30 | onions – 20 |
| peas – 20 | watermelon – 30 |

Rhonda is planning her garden. She decides on the numbers of each vegetable shown on the chart. Create a stem-and-leaf plot on another sheet of paper to find the median and mode number of vegetables she plants.

1. Median number of plants _____

2. Mode number of plants_____

A new off-Broadway show runs for two weeks, for a total of 20 performances. The capacity of the theater is 870 patrons. Create a stem-and-leaf plot on another sheet of paper to determine the median and mode number of attendees.

### Off-Broadway Show Attendance

| performance # | 1 | 2 | 3 | 4 | 5 | 6 | 7 | 8 | 9 | 10 | 11 | 12 | 13 | 14 | 15 | 16 | 17 | 18 | 19 | 20 |
|---|---|---|---|---|---|---|---|---|---|---|---|---|---|---|---|---|---|---|---|---|
| attendance | 870 | 870 | 851 | 845 | 863 | 831 | 846 | 828 | 799 | 856 | 789 | 779 | 800 | 842 | 863 | 865 | 789 | 850 | 870 | 870 |

3. During how many performances was the theater filled to capacity? _____

4. What was the median number of attendees? _____

5. What was the mode number of attendees? _____

6. If you were the producer of this play, would you extend its performance? Why or why not?

_____

_____

Look at these stem-and-leaf plots. What is the median? What is the mode?

| Stem | Leaf |
|---|---|
| 0 | 3 4 4 8 |
| 1 | 6 7 7 9 |
| 2 | 0 1 5 8 8 |
| 3 | 2 2 2 2 6 |
| 4 | 3 7 |

7. Median _____

8. Mode _____

| Stem | Leaf |
|---|---|
| 12 | 0 1 6 7 |
| 13 | 3 4 5 7 |
| 14 | 0 1 1 6 |

9. Median _____

10. Mode _____

•••• **Calculating Median and Mode Using Frequency Charts**

**Directions:** Use what you learned on page 37 to create a frequency chart on another sheet of paper for each set of data below. Use the charts below to calculate the median and mode for each set.

### Electoral Votes Nationwide

| | | | | | | | | | | | | | |
|---|---|---|---|---|---|---|---|---|---|---|---|---|---|
| AL | 9 | GA | 13 | MD | 10 | NJ | 15 | SC | 8 | WY | 3 | | |
| AK | 3 | HA | 4 | MA | 12 | NM | 5 | SD | 3 | | | | |
| AZ | 8 | ID | 4 | MI | 18 | NY | 33 | TN | 11 | | | | |
| AR | 6 | IL | 22 | MN | 10 | NC | 14 | TX | 32 | | | | |
| CA | 54 | IN | 12 | MS | 7 | ND | 3 | UT | 5 | | | | |
| CO | 8 | IA | 7 | MO | 11 | OH | 21 | VT | 3 | | | | |
| CT | 8 | KS | 6 | MT | 3 | OK | 8 | VA | 13 | | | | |
| DC | 3 | KY | 8 | NE | 5 | OR | 7 | WA | 11 | | | | |
| DE | 3 | LA | 9 | NV | 4 | PA | 23 | WV | 5 | | | | |
| FL | 25 | ME | 4 | NH | 4 | RI | 4 | WI | 11 | | | | |

**1.** median number of electoral votes

_____

**2.** mode _____

**3.** median number of years the presidents served ➡ _____

**4.** mode_____

### First Thirty-Two Presidential Terms
### (Number of Years Served as President)

| | | | |
|---|---|---|---|
| Washington | 8 | Johnson, A. | 4 |
| Adams, J. | 4 | Grant | 8 |
| Jefferson | 8 | Hayes | 4 |
| Madison | 10 | Garfield | 1 |
| Monroe | 8 | Arthur | 4 |
| Adams, J. Q. | 4 | Cleveland | 8 |
| Jackson | 8 | Harrison | 4 |
| Van Buren | 4 | McKinley | 4 |
| Harrison | 1 | Roosevelt, T. | 8 |
| Tyler | 4 | Taft | 4 |
| Polk | 4 | Wilson | 8 |
| Taylor | 1 | Harding | 2 |
| Fillmore | 3 | Coolidge | 5 |
| Pierce | 4 | Hoover | 4 |
| Buchanan | 4 | Roosevelt, F. D. | 12 |
| Lincoln | 4 | Truman | 8 |

### Final Medal Standings,
### Winter Olympic Games, 1994

| Country | Gold | Silver | Bronze | Total |
|---|---|---|---|---|
| Norway | 10 | 11 | 5 | 26 |
| Germany | 9 | 7 | 8 | 24 |
| Russia | 11 | 8 | 4 | 23 |
| Italy | 7 | 5 | 8 | 20 |
| United States | 6 | 5 | 2 | 13 |
| Canada | 3 | 6 | 4 | 13 |
| Switzerland | 3 | 4 | 2 | 9 |
| Austria | 2 | 3 | 4 | 9 |
| South Korea | 4 | 1 | 1 | 6 |
| Finland | 0 | 1 | 5 | 6 |
| Japan | 1 | 2 | 2 | 5 |
| France | 0 | 1 | 4 | 5 |
| Netherlands | 0 | 1 | 3 | 4 |
| Sweden | 2 | 1 | 0 | 3 |
| Kazakhstan | 1 | 2 | 0 | 3 |
| China | 0 | 1 | 2 | 3 |
| Slovenia | 0 | 0 | 3 | 3 |
| Ukraine | 1 | 0 | 1 | 2 |
| Belarus | 0 | 2 | 0 | 2 |
| Great Britain | 0 | 0 | 2 | 2 |
| Uzbekistan | 1 | 0 | 0 | 1 |

**5.** median number of total medals _____

**6.** median number of gold medals _____

**7.** median number of silver medals _____

**8.** median number of bronze medals _____

**9.** mode number of total medals _____

**10.** mode number of gold medals _____

| | |
|---|---|
| **median** ⟶ | the number that falls *exactly* in the middle of a set of data that is arranged in order from least to greatest. |
| **mode** ⟶ | the number that appears most frequently in a set of numbers. There may be one, more than one, or no mode. |

**Directions:** Estimate the median and mode for each set of data below.

### Height of Mountains Across the United States

| | |
|---|---|
| McKinley | 20,320 ft. |
| Whitney | 14,494 ft. |
| Blackburn | 16,390 ft. |
| Yale | 14,196 ft. |
| Churchill | 15,638 ft. |
| Hunter | 14,573 ft. |
| Liberty Cap | 14,112 ft. |
| Evans | 14,264 ft. |
| Foraker | 17,400 ft. |
| Castle Peak | 14,265 ft. |

### Size of National Parks (in acres) Across the United States

| | |
|---|---|
| Big Bend | 801,163 |
| Everglades | 1,506,499 |
| Glacier | 1,013,572 |
| Grand Canyon | 1,217,158 |
| Great Smoky Mountains | 520,269 |
| Isle Royale | 571,790 |
| Joshua Tree | 559,955 |
| Kenai Fjords | 669,541 |
| Kings Canyon | 461,901 |
| North Cascades | 504,781 |
| Olympic | 922,651 |
| Sequoia | 402,482 |
| Yosemite | 751,236 |

1. Median height of mountains across the United States _____

2. Mode height of mountains across the United States _____

3. Median acreage of national parks across the United States _____

4. Mode acreage of national parks across the United States _____

**Directions:** Find the number of combinations.

1. A restaurant offers an omelet for breakfast. It can be made by using one egg with a choice of either ham, bacon, or cheese as a filling. How many different combinations are on the menu?

filling

egg

_____

_____

_____

_____ egg x _____ fillings = _____ combinations

2. Mark has a pair of boots and a pair of sneakers. He has one pair of white socks, one pair of black socks, and one pair of brown socks. How many combinations can Mark form?

_____ pairs of shoes x _____ pairs of socks = _____ combinations

3. Karen wants to buy an ice-cream sundae with vanilla ice cream. She has a choice of strawberry, hot fudge, or caramel sauce. Her sundae can be topped with chocolate sprinkles or nuts. How many combinations are there from which to choose?

_____ sauces x _____ toppings = _____ combinations

4. Ben had five television sets in his home. Each set can be tuned to seven channels. How many different combinations can Ben choose from?

_____ televisions x _____ channels = _____ combinations

5. The school cafeteria offers three sandwiches, four vegetables, and five juice drinks daily. How many combinations are available to the students each day?

_____ sandwiches x _____ vegetables x _____ drinks = _____ combinations

You can conduct a simulation to test the results of an outcome. A **simulation** is a simplified experiment. In order for a simulation to work, the possible outcomes of the simulation must match the possible combinations of the actual event.

**Directions:** Use what you learned about combinations on page 41 to describe a simulation for each of the following situations.

You plan to attend a parade where people will throw colored beads to the crowd. You wish to find out if you are likely to receive one color over another. You know that the parade participants have 300 purple beads, 300 blue beads, and 400 pink beads.

Explain your simulation.

_____

_____

_____

_____

You know there are 500 gumballs in the gumball machine. You wish to find out if you are more likely to receive one flavor over another. You know that the machine has 200 cherry, 100 grape, 100 blueberry, and 100 orange gumballs.

Explain your simulation.

_____

_____

_____

_____

_____

A local nursery is giving away free packs of flower seeds, at random, to customers who visit during the month of April. You wish to start a flower garden and you are interested in the free seeds. You wish to find out which type of seeds you are more likely to get. You know the nursery has 25 packs of marigold seeds, 25 petunias, 25 gardenias, 50 mums, and 100 daisies.

Explain your simulation.

_____

_____

_____

_____

_____

Some sets of data include quantities that affect the mean so that the average seems not to represent the data correctly. These quantities, called **outliers**, usually are very different from the other quantities in the set. They can be much larger or smaller than most of the other numbers.

Look at Justin's reading grades.

When a teacher averages grades, she or he usually finds the mean.

**mean grade:** 95

| **Justin's Reading Grades** |
| --- |
| **vocabulary quizzes:** 98, 95, 96 |
| **comprehension tests:** 92, 90, 95 |
| **classwork:** 98, 95, 95, 96 |

Find Justin's other average grades.     **median grade:** 95     **mode grade:** 95

| Grade Scale | |
| --- | --- |
| 100 – 94 | A |
| 93 – 85 | B |
| 84 – 77 | C |
| 76 – 79 | D |
| 69 – 0 | F |

Justin has a high average at this point, as shown by the mean, median, and mode. But what if Justin does poorly on just one vocabulary quiz? Re-average Justin's grades, this time with an additional vocabulary quiz grade of 31.

**mean grade:** 89     **median grade:** 95     **mode grade:** 95

When the teacher averages Justin's grades, she or he will assign him a B even though he has earned an A on most of his class work. Justin's grades are better represented using the median and mode averages instead of the mean. In this set of data, 31 is an **outlier**.

**Directions:** Find the mean, median, and mode for each set of data below. Then, decide which number is the outlier for each set of data.

| Average Number of Points Earned by the Byrd High School Cardinals Girls Basketball Team | | | | |
| --- | --- | --- | --- | --- |
| 64 | 62 | 78 | 64 | 70 |
| 65 | 66 | 64 | 72 | 63 |
| 74 | 31 | 61 | 75 | 66 |

| Average Number of Points Earned by the Byrd High School Cardinals Boys Basketball Team | | | | |
| --- | --- | --- | --- | --- |
| 73 | 78 | 80 | 76 | 74 |
| 74 | 48 | 80 | 78 | 74 |
| 72 | 70 | 74 | 76 | 68 |

1. mean score _____

2. median score _____

3. mode score_____

4. outlier _____

5. mean score _____

6. median score _____

7. mode score _____

8. outlier _____

The **mean**, **median**, and **mode** are all verifiable averages. But sometimes one more clearly represents a set of data better than another.

**Directions:** Use the data in the box below for questions 1 through 5. Calculate the mean, median, and mode. Then, consider the needs of each person's perspective and decide which average is best.

---

### Annual Job Salaries at George's Furniture Business

| | | | | |
|---|---|---|---|---|
| $30,000 | $35,000 | $30,000 | $40,000 | $37,000 |
| $60,000 | $48,000 | $30,000 | $40,000 | $80,000 |

---

**1.** mean: _____

**2.** median: _____

**3.** mode: _____

**4.** If you were George and you're trying to attract the best people to hire, which average would you list in a want ad? Why? _____

_____

**5.** If you were likely to come to work for George, which average salary would you like him to share with you? Why? _____

_____

**6.** A toy company tells you the average cost of a specific kind of doll is $30. Your favorite aunt collects these dolls, and you wish to buy one for her. Do you hope this advertised average is the mean, median, or mode? Why? _____

_____

**7.** If you were the toy company, which average would you advertise to entice more people into the store? _____

_____

**8.** Each of these sets of data below has an average of $30. If you are a comparison shopper, at which store would you shop? Why?_____

_____

| Store A (in dollars) | | | | |
|---|---|---|---|---|
| 35 | 0 | 60 | 50 | 45 |
| 30 | 40 | 80 | 30 | 30 |

| Store B (in dollars) | | | | |
|---|---|---|---|---|
| 10 | 30 | 28 | 22 | 38 |
| 50 | 15 | 45 | 15 | 47 |

| Store C (in dollars) | | | | |
|---|---|---|---|---|
| 28 | 33 | 40 | 45 | 80 |
| 27 | 25 | 28 | 28 | 70 |

**9.** An airline advertises that its pilots have traveled an average of 30,000 flight miles. You think this is a pretty good average. Which average do you hope the airline is advertising, the mean, median, or mode? Why?_____

_____

You can create a spreadsheet file to help organize data averages. This will help you find the median, mode, and range quickly.

Remember, when finding the median, organize the data from least to greatest or greatest to least. Then, find the number in the middle. Organizing data in this manner will also allow you to discover the mode and range quickly.

## Steps to Organizing Data

**First:** Open a spreadsheet program, or open a word processing program where you may insert a spreadsheet file.

**Second:** Enter the data in the first column. Each individual quantity should have its own cell.

**Third:** Find the command that allows you to sort, organize, or arrange data. Selecting ascending order will organize the data from least to greatest. Selecting descending order will organize the data from greatest to least. Either option is acceptable.

**Fourth:** Scan the data to determine the median, mode, and range or set up calculation fields to do this for you.

**Directions:** Open a spreadsheet file and enter the data. Find the median, mode, and range.

**1.** median _____

**2.** mode _____

**3.** range _____

| Data Set 1 | | | | | | | | |
|---|---|---|---|---|---|---|---|---|
| 57 | 35 | 62 | 33 | 34 | 41 | 52 | 64 | 35 |
| 65 | 39 | 33 | 42 | 60 | 46 | 51 | 36 | 61 |
| 38 | 46 | 39 | 52 | 50 | 49 | 33 | | |

**4.** median _____

**5.** mode _____

**6.** range _____

| Data Set 2 | | | | | | | | |
|---|---|---|---|---|---|---|---|---|
| 356 | 289 | 498 | 387 | 398 | 478 | 201 | 480 | 390 |
| 208 | 356 | 498 | 472 | 412 | 322 | 200 | 356 | 409 |
| 289 | 466 | 282 | 356 | 489 | 321 | 234 | | |

The Internet can be a good source to find data. Start off by linking to a search engine and research the information needed about the sharks below. Then, find the mean, median, mode, and range of the data.

**Lengths of Sharks (in meters)**

Tiger _____

Great White_____

Blue_____

Whale _____

Nurse_____

Hammerhead_____

1. mean shark length_____

2. median shark length _____

3. mode shark length_____

4. range of shark lengths_____

Find three other types of sharks and their lengths and list them below. Next, calculate the mean, median, mode, and range a second time using the data above and the new data below.

5. type of shark _____ length _____ (**m**)

6. type of shark _____ length _____ (**m**)

7. type of shark _____ length _____ (**m**)

8. mean_____ 9. median_____ 10. mode_____ 11. range_____

Try calculating this a third time using all the data above except that of the Whale Shark.

**Averages without the whale shark**

12. mean_____

13. median _____

14. mode_____

15. range_____

Are the mean, median, mode, and range in numbers 12–15 much different than numbers 8–11? Why or why not?

_____

_____

**Page 6**
1. I; 0% or 0
2. C; 100% or 1
3. C; 100% or 1
4. C; 100% or 1
5. C; 100% or 1
6. I; 0% or 0
7. C; 100% or 1
8. I; 0% or 0
9. I; 0% or 0
10. I; 0% or 0

**Page 7**
Answers will vary.

**Page 8**
Check students' answers.
1. yes
2. no
3. yes
4. Answers will vary.
5. No. Each event is equally likely.
6. Answers will vary.

**Page 10**
1. 2/5
2. 2/5
3. 1/5
4. 0/5
5. 3/10
6. 2/10 or 1/5
7. 1/10
8. 5/10 or 1/2
9. 5/10 or 1/2
10. John's
11. No. She only has a 1/10 chance.
12. 5/26

13. 21/26
14. 1/26
15. 0/26
16. 9/26
17. 3/26

**Page 11**
1. .1 or .10; 10%
2. .1 or .10; 10%
3. .3 or .30; 30%
4. .3 or .30; 30%
5. .1 or .10; 10%
6. .5 or .50; 50%
7. .4 or .40; 40%
8. .0 or .00; 0%
9. .2 or .20; 20%
10. .5 or .50; 50%

**Page 12**
1. 46/100; 0.46; 46%
2. 7/100; .07; 7%
3. 46/100; .46; 46%
4. 1/50; .02; 2%
5. 34/50; .68; 68%
6. 8/50; .16; 16%
7. carp
8. tin

**Page 14**
1. 8/20 < 12/20
   .4 < .6
   40% < 60%
2. 4/20 < 16/20
   .2 < .8
   20% < 80%
3. 3/20 <17/20
   .15 < .85
   15% < 85%
4. 3/20 <17/20
   .15 < .85
   15% < 85%

5. 5/20 < 15/20
   .25 < .75
   25% < 75%
6. 20/20 > 0/20
   1.0 > 0
   100% > 0%
7. 12/20 > 8/20
   .6 > .4
   60% > 40%
8. 2/20 < 18/20
   .1 < .9
   10% < 90%
9. 0/20 < 20/20
   0 < 1.0
   0% < 100%
10. 10/20 = 10/20
   .5 = .5
   50% = 50%

**Page 15**
1. 35        6. 1/25
2. 30        7. 1/4
3. 42        8. 1/64
4. 400       9. 1/8
5. 1/4

**Page 16**
1. 8
2. 6
3. 72
4. 15; at, as, is, it, us, be, by, do, he, hi, ha, ho, so, to, go

**Page 18**
1. Ronnie's Relics
2. Jerry's Junk House
3. Amy's Afterthoughts and Sarah's Sellables
4. Highest

"Profit to You"; lowest % merchandise sold
5. Answers will vary.

**Page 19**
1. Denver
2. Houston gets nearly twice as much rain as Denver in the same amount of time.
3. Anchorage—clothes for cooler climate; Washington—clothes for warmer climate.
4. Answers will vary.
5. Denver
6. Houston
7. They have similar amounts; slightly higher in Burlington.
8. Answers will vary.

**Page 20**
1. They increase.
2. Likely
3. Almost 100%
4. Insects
5. 1–10%

**Page 22**
1. 8:3; 8 to 3; 8/3
2. 5:6; 5 to 6; 5/6
3. 5:22; 5 to 22; 5/22

4. 22:5; 22 to 5; 22/5
5. 6:8; 6 to 8; 6/8
6. 5:8; 5 to 8; 5/8
7. 3:8; 3 to 8; 3/8
8. 12:15; 12 to 15; 12/15
9. 15:12; 15 to 12; 15/12
10. 10:10; 10 to 10; 10/10
11. 50:15; 50 to 15; 50/15
12. 97:50; 97 to 50; 97/50
13. 10:97; 10 to 97; 10/97
14. 10:10; 10 to 10; 10/10
15. 0:10; 0 to 10; 0/10

**Page 23**
1. chewy and chocolates
2. chewy to cotton or chocolates to cotton or lollipops to fudge
3. rock to sticks
4. fudge to sticks
5. rock to lollipops
6. cotton to fudge
7. 5
8. 25
9. 25
10. 200

**Page 24**
1. 26:26 or 1:1
2. 26:26 or 1:1
3. 13:39 or 1:3
4. 4:48 or 1:12

5. 12:40 or 3:10
6. 48:4 or 12:1
7. 32:20 or 8:5
8. 42:10 or 21:5
9. 52:0
10. 39:13 or 3:1

**Page 26**
1. 4:4      6. 1:4
2. 4:9      7. 1:9
3. 4:4      8. 1:4
4. 4:9      9. No
5. Yes    10. 4
11. Answers will vary.
12. red = 2:6
    blue = 3:5
    green = 3:5
    blue or green

**Page 27**
1. Check students' charts.
2. 27:36
3. 9:36
4. 27:9
5. No
6. Answers will vary.
7. 1:8
8. 1:8
9. 2:6
10. Yes, odds are 1:3, but points are 3:1.

**Page 28**
1. 1,000:1
2. .75 feet or 8 inches
3. 350 feet
4. 75 feet
5. 2.355 feet or about

2 ft. 4 in.
6. Answers will vary.
7.–9. Check students' answers based on #6.

**Page 30**
1. 5
2. 5
3. 14
4. 25
5. 25
6. 57
7. 60
8. 133
9. 583
10. 1,002
11. 1 and 2 or 4 and 5
12. Answers will vary.
13. 91
14. B
15. Answers will vary.
16. Answers will vary.
17. 89
18. B

**Page 31**
1. 10; check graph
2. 12; check graph
3. 7; check graph

**Page 32**
Answers may vary. Approximate answers are:
1. Baltimore, Nashville, or Tampa

2. Reno
3. Baltimore and Nashville
4. about 40 in.
5. about 7 in.
6. about 23 in.
7. about 3 in.
8. about 4 in.
9. about .5 in. or 1 in.
10. 7.3 in.

**Page 34**
1. 6; 3
2. 91; 94
3. 786; 786
4. 26; 19 and 30
5. 40
6. 40
7. $35
8. $15 and $35
9. 25 mpg
10. 32 mpg
11. 25 mpg
12. 37 mpg
13. either; they are the same value
14. median

**Page 35**
1. 37
2. 38.5
3. 60%
4. 20
5. 150
6. 80
7. 100 and 80

**Page 36**
Answers will vary.

**Page 38**
Check students' stem-and-leaf plots
1. 19

2. 20
3. 4
4. 848
5. 870
6. Answers will vary.
7. 23
8. 32
9. 134.5
10. 141

**Page 39**
1. 8    6. 1
2. 3    7. 2
3. 4    8. 2
4. 4    9. 3
5. 5    10. 0

**Page 40**
Answers may vary. Approximate anwers are:
1. 14,000 to 14,999 ft.
2. 14,000 to 14,999 ft.
3. 600,000 to 699,999 ft.
4. 500,000 to 599,999 ft.

**Page 41**
1. 1 egg x 3 fillings = 3 combinations
2. 2 pairs of shoes x 3 pairs of socks = 6 combinations
3. 3 sauces x 2 toppings = 6 combinations
4. 5 televisions x 7 channels = 35 combinations

5. 3 sandwiches x 4 vegetables x 5 drinks = 60 combinations

**Page 42**
Answers will vary.

**Page 43**
1. 65
2. 65
3. 64
4. 31
5. 73
6. 74
7. 74
8. 48

**Page 44**
1. $43,000
2. $38,500
3. $30,000
4. mean
5. mode
6. Answers will vary.
7. the lowest
8.–9. Answers will vary.

**Page 45**
1. 46
2. 33
3. 32
4. 356
5. 356
6. 298

**Page 46**
Answers will vary.